To parents and teachers

We hope you and the children will enjoy reading this story in either English or French. The story is simple, but not *simplified* so the language of the French and the English is quite natural but there is lots of repetition.

At the back of the book is a small picture dictionary with the key words and how to pronounce them. There is also a simple pronunciation guide to the whole story on the last page.

Here are a few suggestions on using the book:

• Read the story aloud in English first, to get to know it. Treat it like any other picture book: look at the pictures, talk about the story and the characters and so on.

• Then look at the picture dictionary and say the French names for the key words. Ask the children to repeat them. Concentrate on speaking the words out loud, rather than reading them.

• Go back and read the story again, this time in English *and* French. Don't worry if your pronunciation isn't quite correct. Just have fun trying it out. Check the guide at the back of the book, if necessary, but you'll soon pick up how to say the French words.

• When you think you and the children are ready, you can try reading the story in French only. Ask the children to say it with you. Only ask them to read it if they are keen to try. The spelling could be confusing and put them off.

• Above all encourage the children to have a go and give lots of praise. Little children are usually quite unselfconscious and this is excellent for building up confidence in a foreign language.

Published by b small publishing ltd.
The Book Shed, 36 Leyborne Park, Kew, Richmond, Surrey, TW9 3HA, UK
www.bsmall.co.uk www.facebook.com/bsmallpublishing @bsmallbear
© b small publishing ltd., 1998. This new edition published 2012
1 2 3 4 5
All rights reserved.
Design: *Lone Morton and Louise Millar*   Editorial: *Catherine Bruzzone and Susan Martineau*
Production: *Madeleine Ehm*
Colour reproduction: *Vimnice Printing Press Co. Ltd.* Printed in China by *WKT Co. Ltd.*
ISBN: 978-1-905710-09-6
British Library Cataloguing in Publication Data. A catalogue record for this book is available from the British Library.

What's for supper?

Qu'est-ce qu'on mange ce soir?

Mary Risk

Pictures by Carol Thompson
French by Christophe Dillinger

b small publishing

We're cooking the supper tonight, Mum.

C'est *nous* qui allons préparer le dîner ce soir, maman.

It's going to be a surprise.

Ça va être une surprise.

Do we need cheese?

Il nous faut du fromage?

Yes, we need cheese, and ham too.

Oui, il nous faut du fromage et
aussi du jambon.

Do we need flour?

Il nous faut de la farine?

Yes.

Oui.

What about potatoes?
Do we need them?

Et des pommes de terre?
Il nous en faut?

No, we don't need potatoes.

Non, on n'a pas besoin de pommes de terre.

But we need tomatoes
and mushrooms.

Mais il nous faut des tomates et
des champignons.

Let's put some olives in it!

Mettons-y des olives!

Oh no! I don't like olives.

Ah non! Je n'aime pas les olives.

How much is all that?

C'est combien tout ça?

What are you going to make?
Please tell me. Please!

No! It's a surprise!

Qu'est-ce que vous allez préparer?
Allez, dites-moi, s'il vous plaît!

Non! C'est une surprise!

Here we are home again.

Nous voilà rentrés à la maison.

Don't come into the kitchen, Mum.

N'entre pas dans la cuisine, maman.

Supper's ready. It's…

Le dîner est prêt. C'est…

a pizza!

une pizza!

Pronouncing French

Don't worry if your pronunciation isn't quite correct. The important thing is to be willing to try. The pronunciation guide here will help but it cannot be completely accurate:

• Read the guide as naturally as possible, as if it were British English.

• Put stress on the letters in *italics*, e.g. from*aj*.

• Don't roll the r at the end of the word, for example in the French word **le** (the): ler.

If you can, ask a French person to help and move on as soon as possible to speaking the words without the guide.

Note French adjectives usually have two forms, one for masculine and one for feminine nouns. They often look very similar but are pronounced slightly differently, e.g. **prêt** and **prête** (see below).

Words Les Mots

leh moh

to cook supper

préparer le dîner

prehpah-*reh* ler deen*eh*

tonight

ce soir

ser swah

surprise

la surprise

lah s-yoor*preez*

cheese

le fromage

ler from*aj*

ham

le jambon

ler shom*boh*

flour

la farine

lah far-*een*

tomato

la tomate

lah tom*at*

potato

la pomme de terre

lah pom der *tair*

olive

l'olive

lol*eev*

mushroom

le champignon

ler shom-peen-*yoh*

pizza

la pizza

lah peet*zah*

ready

prêt/prête

preh/pret

home/house
la maison
lah may*zoh*

mum
maman
ma-*moh*

dad
papa
pa-*pah*

kitchen
la cuisine
la kwee*zeen*

yes
oui
wee

no
non
noh

please
s'il te plaît/
s'il vous plaî
seel ter pleh/seel voo pleh

A simple guide to pronouncing this French story

Qu'est-ce qu'on mange ce soir?
*kes*koh monsh ser swah

C'est *nous* qui allons préparer
seh *noo* kee al-*oh* prehpah-*reh*

le dîner ce soir, maman.
ler deen*eh* ser swah, ma-*moh*

Ça va être une surprise.
sah vah *etr'* yoon s-yoor*preez*

Il nous faut du fromage?
eel noo fo dew from*aj*

Oui, il nous faut du fromage
wee, eel noo fo dew from*aj*

et aussi du jambon.
eh oh*see* dew shom*boh*

Il nous faut de la farine?
eel noo fo der lah far-*een*

Oui.
wee

Et des pommes de terre?
et deh pom der *tair*

Il nous en faut?
eel noozoh fo

Non, on n'a pas besoin de pommes de terre.
noh, oh nah pah b'zwah der pom der *tair*

Mais il nous faut des tomates
meh eel noo fo deh tom*at*

et des champignons.
eh deh shom-peen-*yoh*

Mettons-y des olives!
met-o*zee* dez*oleev*

Ah non! Je n'aime pas les olives.
ah noh, sh' nem pah lez*oleev*

C'est combien tout ça?
seh kombee-*yah* too sah

Qu'est-ce que vous allez préparer?
*kes*ker voozal-*eh* prehpah-*reh*

Allez, dites-moi, s'il vous plaît!
al-*eh*, deet mwah seel voo pleh

Non! C'est une surprise!
noh, set yoon s-yoor*preez*

Nous voilà rentrés à la maison.
noo vwah-*lah* ront*reh* ah lah may*zoh*

N'entre pas dans la cuisine, maman.
nontr' pah doh lah kwee*zeen*, ma-*moh*

Le dîner est prêt. C'est...
ler deen*eh* eh preh, seh

une pizza!
yoon peet*sah*